The OP Book

by Lynn Maslen Kertell
pictures by Sue Hendra and John R. Maslen

Scholastic Inc.
New York • Toronto • London • Auckland • Sydney • Mexico City • New Delhi • Hong Kong • Buenos Aires

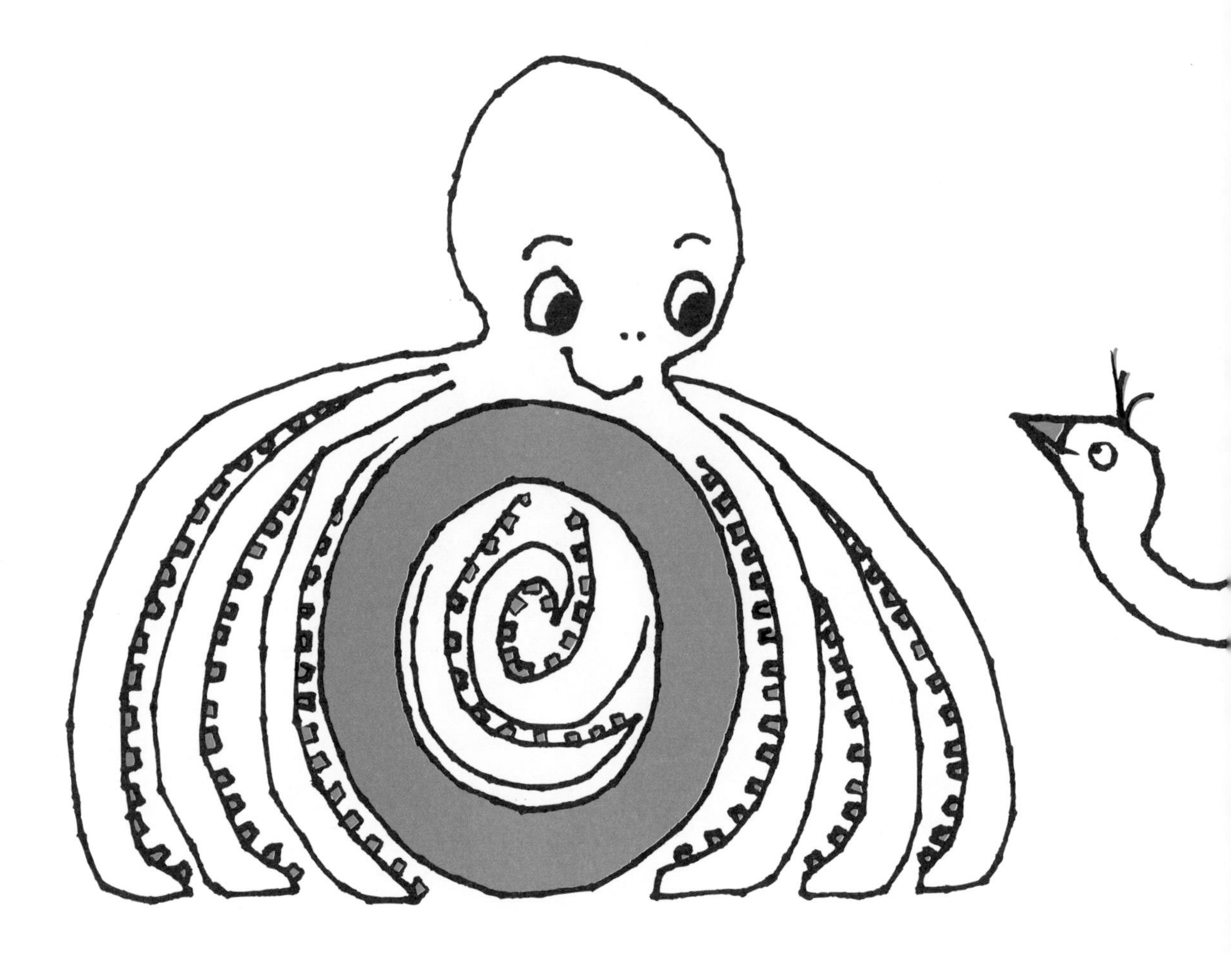

Octopus

ostriches

Octopus and ostrich

have each other's overalls!

Pig

puppy

Portly pigs like

plenty of pie.

Octopus and ostrich

join the pigs for pie!

Look for these **o** and **p** words in this book.

octopus	pie
ostrich(es)	pig(s)
other's	plenty
overalls	portly
	puppy

Look for these additional **o** and **p** words in the pictures: owl, orange, pans, pastry, paws, pears, piglet, pineapple, plate, and pockets.